FOR GARTH!

— YUKO & ANANTH !

JOHNNY WANDER VOLUME 1: DON'T BURN THE HOUSE DOWN

Diligently written by Ananth Panagariya.
Lovingly illustrated by Yuko Ota.

Indispensable people: George Rohac, Keith Wood & Erica Moen. And our parents, of course. Thanks!

First edition: September 2010.
ISBN-10: 0-9785016-1-6
ISBN-13: 978-0-9785016-1-7

5 4 3 2 1

Printed in the U.S.A.

Portions of this book are published online at www.johnnywander.com. This volume collects the first Johnny Wander comics, posted online between September 30, 2008 and October 6, 2009.

This book is dedicated to

Johnny Wander wouldn't be what it is without your hard work. Thanks for being our developer, Conrad! And John, thanks for the product photos and the thousand and one little things you give us a hand with. And thank you both, for allowing us to plunder your lives for the funny stuff.

INTRODUCTION

Johnny Wander is a rendering of the imagination. Here is the true story:

Conrad is a retired vampire hunter turned mercenary. He's roughly 50 years old, although it's impossible to be sure till you cut him open and count the rings. He drops into military hot zones with just a flak jacket and his bare hands - his MO is OSP.

John is an advanced AI working for the FBI. He specializes in the capture of robots that kill serial killers that kill robots. He hasn't seen a lot of time in the field, but just wait. The future is coming.

Yuko is a beastmaster, friend of animals real and mythologic. **Especially** mythologic. She knows everything the woods know, and the woods know **all** about you.

As for myself, there's not much to say. Space isn't as cold as you'd think.

The comics presented herein are works of fiction. Believe what you will.

-Ananth
Asteroid M over Brooklyn, NY 2010

FOREWORD

If this is your first time laying eyes on Johnny Wander you're in for a treat. For those of you who have never read Johnny Wander before, no one named Johnny Wander was involved or influenced the project. The creative team behind this beautiful little package is Ananth Panagariya and Yuko Ota, two wildly talented individuals who are regrettably younger than me.

When they first told me about their idea for Johnny Wander I got rather excited. It's their first project as a team, and their previous work is strong separately. The result is a whimsical slice-of-life series that manages to stand out as being wholesome and funny all at the same time. Ananth manages to write a humorous strip derived from real life that doesn't fall into the trap of "had to be there", and happily avoids being laden with post-modern irony, while Yuko's visual adaptations of their friends and family pop off the page with an animated sense of style that can be compared to works such as Meredith Gran's Octopus Pie or Bryan Lee O'Malley's Scott Pilgrim.

Those of you who have read Johnny Wander online - you're already won over. You know how much fun it is to read these comics. The care and effort put into them is obvious. That's why you've picked this book up.

Now enough talk, let's get to some comics!

With humble regards, I am,
George Rohac Jr
Operations Director, Oni Press
-July 2010

I.

I WISH to go a'wanderin',
A' wanderin' with you

What won'drous woods and wilderness
We'll go a'traipsing through

What kinds of creatures shall we see?
A'wanderin', jus' you an me?
Birds and beasts from land and sea

While wanderin' with you.

sage advice

his parents must be so proud

☆ BREAKFAST: 24/7
☆ EXHIBITIONISM: 80%
☆ SCOTT PILGRIM: TOTALLY

a valid point

Puck Fair

salted plum

rest in pieces

conrad's fourteen new friends

COMRADE CONRAD
SPX 2008 ROCKVILLE MD

How it happened, in murky recollection: After the show, people head over to a nearby karaoke place. Somewhere between 11 PM and midnight Yuko and I hit the road. Conrad sticks around.

11:47 PM
Conrad realizes that he only knows two people there. He decides he needs to make some friends and starts buying drinks from Diane, the flirty bartender.

12:17 AM
Diane the booze angel takes a shine to our plucky hero. She begins to pour out free drinks, to the tune of,

1:00 AM
3 firewaters

1:33 AM
Something red, white and blue (Conrad dubbed it 'The Patriot')

2:21 AM
Terrible Korean sake

2:30 AM
14 stoplights in shot glasses
2 stoplights in martini glasses

Conrad lives through this and tells us all about it the next morning. We curse ourselves for leaving early - quietly, out of respect for his hangover.

If you spend a night out with Conrad, you'll most likely have an adventure. It's just how he does business, whether on purpose or by accident.

boys are wimps

abandonment

an open letter to all
US registered voters

spreading the wealth around

exxxtreme furniture purchases

rest in pieces redux

then i got curtains

in the walls

WELL, WE FINISHED MOVING IN.
SPACKLEHAUS MEMOIRS 1
HOW'S IT LOOK?
o-okay....
AW, WHAT'S UP?
THERE'S A HIDDEN ROOM—
I CAN SEE THE WINDOW FROM THE OUTSIDE, BUT THERE'S NO WAY TO GET TO IT...
I...
I think the house is haunted.
WANT ME TO STAY ON THE PHONE WITH YOU?
NO...
skrch
skitter
skitter
skitter
skrch
yes.

ghosts might have been preferable

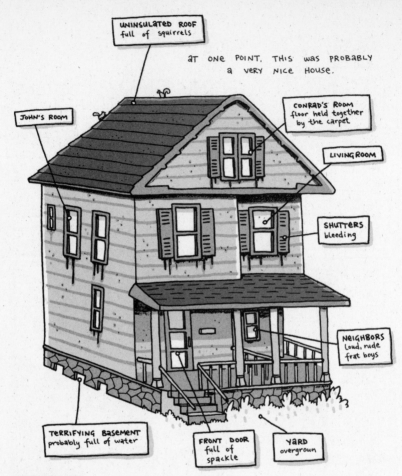

UNINSULATED ROOF
full of squirrels

AT ONE POINT, THIS WAS PROBABLY
A VERY NICE HOUSE.

CONRAD'S ROOM
floor held together
by the carpet

JOHN'S ROOM

LIVING ROOM

SHUTTERS
bleeding

NEIGHBORS
loud, rude
frat boys

TERRIFYING BASEMENT
probably full of water

FRONT DOOR
full of
spackle

YARD
overgrown

SPACKLEHAUS

Spacklehaus (pronounced Spackle-house) is a fabled old house located on a quiet neighborhood street in Rochester, NY. Think back to your childhood, to the dilapidated house that you were certain was haunted and was there a ghost in the window that one night oh shit oh shit!! That's Spacklehaus, except it turns out it's not terribly scary … just really, really shitty. Everything is old and possibly falling apart. All the floors bow underneath the carpet. The back stairs are narrow and steep and very long - someone died on those stairs, for sure. The back of the basement door is pockmarked and splattered with red paint. Y-yeah …, paint … And of course, the landlord fixes everything with spackle.

Despite all these things, there was something charming about that Spacklehaus. Just don't ask us to admit that out loud.

the best sleep over ever

the first plague

he only likes fake coffee

the most obvious course of action

theasaur

a netflix for books

guilty until proven guilty

our neighbors think we are weird

STOP EATING RIBBONS

read instructions before proceeding

akemashite omedetou gozaimasu

あけましておめでとうございます。
happy new year

GOBO

DAIKON

SALMON

RENKON — pickled lotus root.

THE LOTUS FLOWER HAS TIES TO BUDDHA AND THEREFORE IS ASSOCIATED WITH GODLY BLESSINGS.

ZONI — mochi soup.

A TRADITIONAL SOUP MADE WITH RICE CAKE AND FOODS FROM THE THREE HARVESTED REGIONS OF JAPAN: MOUNTAINS, FIELDS, AND OCEAN. THIS IS MY FAMILY'S RECIPE.

INARIZUSHI — sushi rice in a sweet fried tofu shell.

ASSOCIATED WITH THE RICE GODDESS, INARI — IT IS SUPPOSED TO BE A FAVORED FOOD OF HER MESSENGER FOXES.

ZENZAI — sweet azuki bean and mochi soup

EATING RED THINGS ON NEW YEARS IS SUPPOSED TO BRING GOOD FORTUNE. (A HANDFUL OF PEOPLE DIE EVERY NEW YEAR BY CHOKING ON MOCHI.)

not the first time this has happened

YOU HAVE TO MAKE IT REALLY BAD

happy birthday conrad

various inadequacies

fifth sense

what was i supposed to say

zoo LOLOLogy

without cable we cannot be sure anyway

three dollar comfort

MAKE A HEATING PAD

1. Take a bandana and fold it in half.

2. Sew along the edges to create one long pocket. Turn it inside out so the seams are on the inside.

3. Begin filling the pocket with rice. You can use cheap parboiled rice with a few bags of fragrant tea, or lavender, or whatever.

4. When you've filled it about a quarter of the way, sew the section shut. Fill the next section with rice. Repeat.

6. To use: microwave it! Don't microwave for more than a minute at a time.

7. Make some tea, put on some warm socks, and relax. v

incorrect bread anatomy

initial y

pink and purple pointsetta socks

haircut tax

cake wreck

KING CAKE

We stumbled upon a King Cake at the grocery store in Rockville, MD and it was a baffling experience. For those as ignorant as us: Imagine a ring cake with sprinkles, sickly easter-colored frosting and a small plastic baby.

A King Cake, as it turns out, is a festival cake associated with various holidays around the world. In the U.S. it's commonly seen during Mardi Gras. The plastic baby - or trinket, whatever it may be - is meant to be baked into the cake, hidden away. The person who gets the baby in their slice is given certain privileges, and certain responsibilities - chief among which is that they must bring the cake next year.

Wikipedia says:

"THE KING CAKE OF THE NEW ORLEANS MARDI GRAS TRADITION COMES IN A NUMBER OF STYLES. THE MOST SIMPLE, SAID TO BE THE MOST TRADITIONAL, IS A RING OF TWISTED BREAD SIMILAR TO THAT USED IN BRIOCHE TOPPED WITH ICING OR SUGAR, USUALLY COLORED PURPLE, GREEN, AND GOLD (THE TRADITIONAL CARNIVAL COLORS) WITH FOOD COLORING. THERE ARE MANY VARIANTS, SOME WITH A FILLING, THE MOST COMMON BEING CREAM CHEESE AND PRALINE. CAJUN KING CAKES ARE TRADITIONALLY DEEP FAT FRIED AS A DOUGHNUT WOULD BE. THEY ARE TOPPED WITH SUGAR GRANULES IN THE OFFICIAL CARNIVAL COLORS OF PURPLE, GREEN AND GOLD. THE PURPLE REPRESENTS THE PASSION OF CHRIST, THE GREEN REPRESENTS HOPE AND THE GOLD THE REWARDS OF LEADING A CHRISTIAN LIFE."

It was actually our readers who clued us in on this after the comic (left) went up, which occasionally happens. More often, we'll share a story, and then our readers will share their own stories, which is sometimes more interesting (to us) than creating the comics that start the conversation.

he named the houseplants

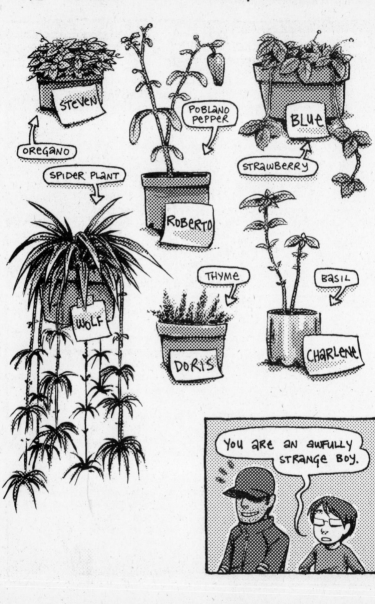

latitude change

inscrutable language joke

MAN, I LOVE YOUR DAD'S SUKIYAKI.

MORE LIKE DAISUKI-YAKI, AMIRITE?

where Yuko has to explain the joke:

鋤 焼き = SUKIYAKI, BEEF HOT POT.
PLOW   COOK

大 好き = DAISUKI, TO LOVE
BIG LIKE

her computer died

homemade mace

FIRE

The running theme when we lived in Rockville was fire. It was in the name of the complex, and there were in fact fireplaces in each of the apartments. The flues were welded shut a long time ago, so they were purely ornamentation at that point. The complex got a lot of visits from the fire department because people tried using the fireplaces anyway - their apartments filled up with smoke and the alarms went off.

We ourselves were guilty of setting the smoke detector off, but for different reasons - Yuko was growing peppers all year, and we wanted to dry some of them to make cracked red pepper. So, uh, we put them in the oven. It didn't work out. There was no slow burn - suddenly there was smoke and it was burning, and once it started it only got worse. The worst (best) part was watching John fight through the smoke to turn the oven off.

And man oh man, it really did feel like mace.

yuko's parents' cats again

things mika likes to do:

drink from wet hair | destroy things while no one is looking | sleep on people, sometimes

things gonta likes to do:

fret | eat | fret

things they both like to do:

run around in the small hours of the morning

a face like sandpaper

give or take ten years

get ripped quick

ANANTH: 10 pullups

CONRAD: 7 pullups

JOHN: 7 pullups

YUKO: 3/4 pullup

you were boat-adopted

aaaaaaaaa

REM cooking

REM cooking

DREAM CURRY

This recipe makes enough curry for 6 or more hungry people, with leftovers. An excellent "bachelor" recipe. It's quick to put together, you don't have to watch it, you really can't overcook it unless you're trying... there aren't a lot of ways to mess this up.

Makes one giant 6 quart pot of curry

INGREDIENTS
x2, large chicken breasts, cubed (or more)
x1, 15 oz can of pumpkin puree
x1, 15 oz can of reduced sodium chicken broth
x1, 8 oz box of S&B Golden Curry
x~4 carrots, peeled and cut into bite-sized pieces
x~3 big potatoes, peeled & cut into pieces
x1 large onion, cut into large pieces
x~2 garlic cloves, diced
x~1 tbsp ginger (grated fresh or dried)
cream or milk to taste

INSTRUCTIONS
1. Add all ingredients (except milk) to slow cooker
2. Just barely cover all ingredients with water
3. Cover and cook on high for 4-5 hours or low on 6-8 hours, stirring every few hours
4. Add cream if desired

Feel free to add or replace any vegetables. This will probably taste good with tomato, apple, sweet potato, peas, squash, eggplant, pepper, or whatever. There's no right way to make it.

If you want, you can eat the curry plain. Traditionally, you eat it over Japanese sticky rice, but you can also put the curry over regular white rice, ramen noodles, spaghetti, or whatever else you might want.

This is an ideal winter meal. It's stick-to-your-ribs warm and it'll keep in your freezer for-ev-er.

john sets more things on fire

THE CONTEST

Back when this comic came out, Conrad cooked up a web app that allowed people to submit their own dialogue for the strip. We held a contest to see who could come up with the funniest remix. Here are some winners:

desperate times

also there was a comic convention

A SAGA

Kanye West's album Graduation comes out. John calls Conrad 'Conye'.

We go to New York for a weekend and stop at St. Mark's. A vendor is selling the Kanye West shutter glasses from the Stronger video. They are really dumb. Naturally, we buy them.

Back in Rockville, Conrad puts on the glasses and records a short webcam video. He posts it on 12seconds.tv: "Hey ... the guys went up to New York and bought me these ballin' glasses. Thanks guys. Really."

We do a strip about the glasses, and Conrad posts a link to the video in the blogpost. His video shoots up to the #1 spot overnight.

BT is a top-selling electronica artist, one of Conrad's favorites. He's posting videos to the same website, and has been trying to get to the top spot for months. Stymied, BT investigates the punk kid who has the top spot with his video about some stupid glasses. Conrad's 12seconds account leads to his website which leads to his resume which leads to his number. Conrad's phone rings.

C: "Hello?"
BT: "Hi, this is BT."
C: " .... "
BT: "I'm a musician? You might have heard of me ..."
C: " ... yes I know who you are."
BT: "Oh!"
C: "I uh ... I just want to say that I really like your stuff."
BT: "Oh, thank you!"
C: " ... "
BT: " ... "
C: " ... "
BT: "You have some skills I'm looking for. I want to offer you a job ..."

best left unanswered

luckily they are all nerdy

natural defense mechanisms

a lesson in appropriate attire

she was pretty angry

STEEL NIBS AND I
ARE BREAKING UP.

she only likes real coffee

flights and flights of stairs

then again, it's probably engrish

A DAY IN JAPAN: From Yuko's Travel Journal

WE SPENT THE MORNING VISITING GRAVES.

UNAGI DON FOR LUNCH

MET a NICE DOG

foxes in the backyard

silly hats only

CUTE THINGS WE'VE SEEN ON THE SUBWAY LATELY

a weekend at connecticon

that can't be comfortable

at least we can be assured that Gonta will never be eaten by dinosaurs.

his pride, her passion

THERE WAS A WOMAN READING A
ROMANCE NOVEL ON THE METRO.

SHE WAS AT ONE OF THE STEAMY PARTS.

one bunny rabbit....

i still have to make bunny-ears to tie my shoes.

AIRPLANES

I love flying. My folks got me started early - we went to India every two years, over summer vacations. Those biennial trips were bracketed by airplane gauntlets, where we would spend a total of 18+ hours in the air, often in the space of 24 hours.

It was around hour 4 or 5 that all conventional entertainment was exhausted. My brother and I would pack some books or our handheld Tiger TMNT game or our sketchbooks, but the entertainment value in all those distractions would inevitably peter out. My parents always kept a deck of cards on hand, and so we staved boredom off for another hour or two in that way. We'd kill some time sleeping, but what I'm getting at is that eventually you hit those last hours where you'd begin to feel that you were going to spend the rest of your life in that airplane, pacing up and down the aisles. Those last hours defied physics, expanding into ranges beyond human cognition. You held onto sanity with a fingernail.

Did I say I love flying? Hmm.

sacks of potatoes

parental supervision required

so dumb

pardon our dust

stairs forever

we now live on the top floor

of a five-story building

with no elevators.

it seemed like a good idea at the time.

the most terrible thing

at least it wasn't your head

I SWEAR, THIS IS GONNA HAPPEN ONE OF THESE DAYS.

well, maybe your head would've been better

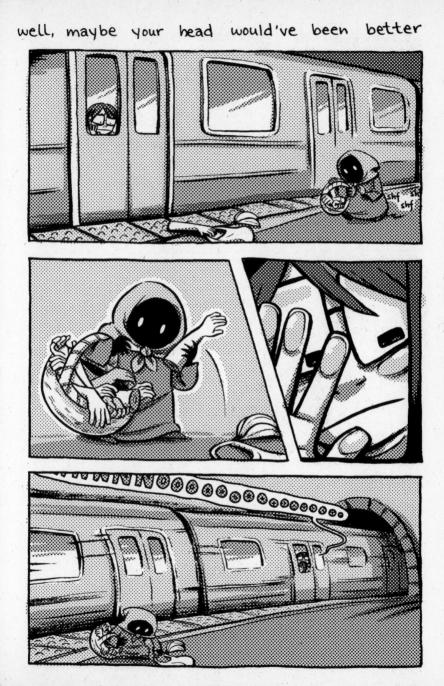

laundromat friends

Jorge

and There's a tree in the park and a squirrel and a Mommy bird bringing a worm to its babies — and there are eggs in the nest too and there's a slide and some one riding it — no it's too short — yeah

Wow, I'm such a good artist!

from planet panagarixa 7

BEFORE A WEDDING IN SOUTH CAROLINA

DID YOU GET THE RIGHT TUX?

Y-YEAH, BUT THEY SPELLED MY NAME FUNNY...

FANCY PLACE
TUXEDO RENTALS
5000 ROAD ST
PLACETOWN, NC
OXSAB, USA

DATE 6/30

AMNANTH PANAGARIXA

NAME _____

LEDDING PARTY

RCH

welcome to earth!

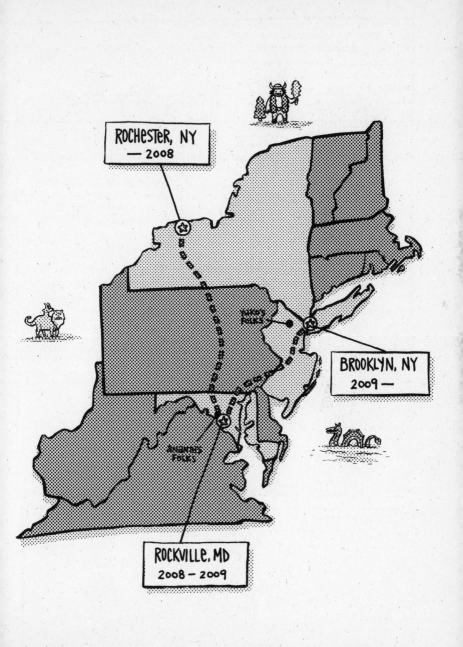

ROCHESTER, NY
— 2008

BROOKLYN, NY
2009 —

ROCKVILLE, MD
2008 — 2009

EXTRAS

Back before Johnny Wander was on the web, we did some test strips to suss out what it was we wanted these autobio comics to be about, especially in terms of tone. You'll notice some of these read less "Johnny Wander" than others!

This was before we moved to Brooklyn - I think we were visiting my folks. A test of format - the first of many - and we ultimately passed on it. You can tell a story in one panel, but we wanted something with a little more flex.

7/30/07 — ANANTH AND YUKO GO SHOPPING IN NYC.

I was never a big fan of this format, wherein the page is wider than it is tall. The strip itself also felt a little negative.

A little negative, again. We were feeling more and more that JW ought to hit a light-hearted note. It also felt like there was only half a story here.

A lot of problems with this one. The geek reference felt stale - this is a conversation we had in real life so it fits the autobio mold, but there are a lot of people already doing this (and doing it better). Comics like Yotsuba&! have a universal appeal that doesn't require an encyclopedic geek knowledge, and that's what we began striving for.

It also felt way too personal - we don't hide the fact that we're dating, but prefer to keep it secondary within the comic.

Again, waaay too personal. Also more words than we normally use.

We hit upon the right tone here! This comic was actually redone as an "official" JW comic (page 97).

This one also got redone (page 53). although I really like the original!

OMING SOON

Lucky Penny from Oni Press in 2011
Johnny Wander Vol. 2 in 2011

OTHER WORK

Callie Eats Feathers in MDHP Vol. 5 from Dark Horse Comics
ISBN-10 1595825703, ISBN-13 978-1595825704

ANANTH
Applegeeks Volume 1 from Dark Horse Comics
ISBN-10 1595821740, ISBN-13 978-1595821744

Applegeeks Volume 2 from Dark Horse Comics
ISBN-10 1595823379, ISBN-13 978-1595823373

Robro in MDHP Vol. 4 from Dark Horse Comics
ISBN-10 1595823271 ISBN-13 978-1595823274

www.applegeeks.com

YUKO
Manga Math 4 from Lerner Publishing
ISBN-10 0761352457 ISBN-13 978-0761352457

Twisted Journeys: Detective Frankenstein from Lerner Publishing
ISBN-10 0822589435 ISBN-13 978-0822589433

YUKO OTA is a freelance cartoonist and illustrator who has worked with publishers like Oni Press, Lerner Publishing and Dark Horse, Inc. She works in a cozy home office somewhere in Brooklyn, NY. Her assistant is a little black cat, who diligently steals her seat and picks up the slack on her sleep schedule. Yuko is powered by coffee, usually with a dash of milk and a dollop of molasses.

In addition to her normal workload, Yuko volunteers. She spends most of her community service hours in the U.S. dealing with domestic crises, except for a brief stint overseas assisting Excalibur.

ANANTH PANAGARIYA is a writer, designer, and reader who has written and produced work for Oni Press and Dark Horse, Inc. He spent 2008 designing and branding Snapture, an iPhone app that was featured in WIRED, Engadget, the Financial Times and the Wall Street Journal. Much of his design work since has been t-shirt design, a passion of his. Ananth is usually putting pencil to paper, analog or otherwise.

If you ask him about the Weapon X program, he'll tell you it wasn't as bad as everyone says. There was a lot of down time, during which the Weapon X subjects engaged in rap battles and slam poetry.

COMING SOON

Lucky Penny from Oni Press in 2011
Johnny Wander Vol. 2 in 2011

OTHER WORK

Callie Eats Feathers in MDHP Vol. 5 from Dark Horse Comics
ISBN-10 1595825703, **ISBN-13** 978-1595825704

ANANTH
Applegeeks Volume 1 from Dark Horse Comics
ISBN-10 1595821740, **ISBN-13** 978-1595821744 .

Applegeeks Volume 2 from Dark Horse Comics
ISBN-10 1595823379, **ISBN-13** 978-1595823373

Robro in MDHP Vol. 4 from Dark Horse Comics
ISBN-10 1595823271 **ISBN-13** 978-1595823274

www.applegeeks.com

YUKO
Manga Math 4 from Lerner Publishing
ISBN-10 0761352457 **ISBN-13** 978-0761352457

Twisted Journeys: Detective Frankenstein from Lerner Publishing
ISBN-10 0822589435 **ISBN-13** 978-0822589433